The Blue Scooter

W0009695

Frank had a brand new, blue
scooter. It glinted in the sun.
The scooter was cool.

Alf had an old, blue scooter. It was his dad's. His blue scooter was not so cool.

"Let's have a contest," said Frank.
"OK," said Alf, but he knew that
Frank's scooter was faster.

The rabbits took the scooters
to the top of the hill. Frank's
scooter flew past Alf's scooter.

As Frank zoomed down the hill,
he hit a bump. He flew off his
scooter and landed in the mud.

Alf got screws from his tool box
to fix Frank's blue scooter.

"You are a true pal!" said Frank.

Questions for discussion:

- Why do you think Frank had an accident?

- What did Alf do when Frank fell off his scooter?

- What would you do if you were Alf?

Game with /oo/ words

Play as 'Concentration' or use for reading practice. Enlarge and photocopy the page twice on two different colors of card.
Cut the cards up to play.
Ensure the players sound out the words.

moon	blue	drew
flew	broom	true
troop	glue	grew
clue	threw	stool

Before reading this book, the reader needs to know:

- sounds can be spelled by more than one letter.
- the spellings <oo>, <ew> and <ue> can represent the sound /oo/.

This book introduces:

- the spellings <oo>, <ew> and <ue> for the sound /oo/.
- text at 2-syllable level.

Words the reader may need help with:

scooter, was, old, so, said, OK, knew, faster, took, down, you, are

Vocabulary:

brand new – completely new
glinted   – shone in the sunlight
contest   – competition

Talk about the story:

Frank has a brand new scooter.
Alf has an old scooter.
The rabbits have a race.
Can you guess what happens?

Reading Practice

Practice blending these sounds into words:

oo	ew	ue
cool	flew	blue
moon	blew	clue
boot	drew	true
tool	crew	glue
soon	grew	Sue
room	chew	untrue
spoon	threw	bluebell